for all my family and friends

TOMMY'S SCOTTISH ISLAN

Go island hopping with Tommy and enjoy magical music from magical islands!

Ten traditional Scottish island tunes for the young music maker. Sing the tunes or play on violin, keyboard, accordion, pipes, whistle, recorder or other instruments. A wonderful selection for family and friends to 'join in'. Also ideal for the classroom with background information and island drawings adding interest and intrigue!

Have fun with Tommy's Quiz, Tommy's Tips, his Memory Tune and of course Tommy's Own Tune – and colour in the drawings if you want to!

Compiled, chosen and adapted by Joyce McIver
Drawings by Andrew Magee
Map drawings by Iain McIver
Published by Leckie & Leckie 2002

ISBN   1-898890-24-2

Dear Young Music Maker,

Hello, I'm very pleased to meet you!

My name is Tommy McTavish and I come from Falkland, a wee village in Fife, in the east of Scotland.

I just love to play and sing my tunes. Sometimes I play and my friends sing. Sometimes I play and my family sing.

Sometimes I practise very hard on my own! But I always have great fun!

I hope *you* have great fun learning all my Scottish island tunes!

Look out for my paw prints – they might help you! Happy playing, happy singing and happy island hopping! Lots of love,

Tommy

CONTENTS

'Here is my very own tune – I hope you like it! You can play it or sing it as a round.
Start each part at my paw print.' 🐾 Tommy

Tommy's Own Tune

Joyce McIver

Brightly

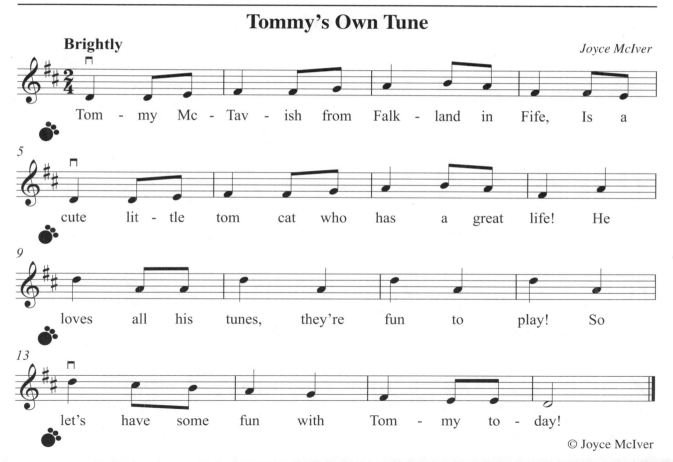

Tom - my Mc - Tav - ish from Falk - land in Fife, Is a

cute lit - tle tom cat who has a great life! He

loves all his tunes, they're fun to play! So

let's have some fun with Tom - my to - day!

Tommy says 'This tune starts an adventurous journey to some of the islands in Scotland. Take care with all the dotted rhythms – especially the *Scotch snap* ♫. and remember to go back to the fancy sign!'

Tune 1

The Road to the Isles

Words: Kenneth MacLeod
Music: John McLellan

Lively, like a march

D.S. al Fine

A far croonin' is pullin' me away
As take I wi' my *cromak* to the road,
The far *Coolins* are puttin' love on me
As step I wi' the sunlight for my load.

Sure, by Tummel and Loch Rannoch and Lochaber I will go,
By heather tracks wi' heaven in their wiles;
If it's thinkin' in your inner heart and *braggart's* in my step,
You've never smelt the tangle o' the Isles.

Oh, the far Coolins are puttin' love on me,
As step I wi' my cromak to the Isles.

cromak: crook-handled walking stick
Coolins (usually spelt Cuillins): the Cuillin Hills are on the
Island of Skye
braggart: swagger

Tommy says 'If you can, with your pencil please, carefully name the notes of this tune. Start at my single paw print. 🐾 (Ignore the letters above the notes – these are for piano or guitar accompaniment.)'

Tune 2   Skye Boat Song

Words: Sir Harold Boulton
Tune: Traditional

Speed bonnie boat like a bird on the wing,
Onward the sailors cry;
Carry the lad that's born to be king
Over the sea to Skye.

Loud the winds howl, loud the waves roar,
Thunderclaps rend the air;
Baffled our foes stand by the shore,
Follow they will not dare.

Speed bonnie boat etc.

Though the waves leap, soft shall ye sleep,
Ocean's a royal bed.
Rocked in the deep Flora will keep
Watch by your weary head.

Speed bonnie boat etc.

The words here tell how in the winter of 1745–1746 Bonnie Prince Charlie escaped from his enemies. The brave Flora Macdonald smuggled him 'over the sea to Skye' from Benbecula, the island between North Uist and South Uist.

Tune 3

Uist Tramping Song

Words: Hugh S. Roberton
Tune: John R. Bannerman

At a steady pace

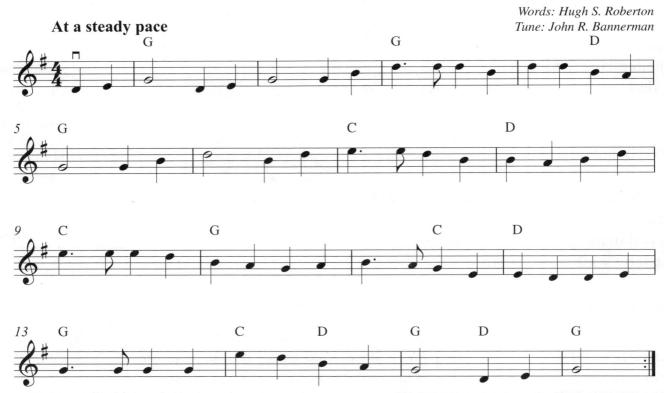

Permission kindly granted by Roberton Publications

Come along, come along, let us foot it out together;
Come along, come along, be it fair or stormy weather;
With the hills of home before us and the purple of the heather,
Let us sing in happy chorus, come along, come along!

(sing twice)

'Here is my Island Memory Tune. This means I can play it without looking at the music. Carefully learn the tune and see if you can play it by memory. If it helps, name the notes with your pencil first. Good luck and keep trying!' Tommy

Tune 4

Eriskay Love Lilt

Marjory Kennedy-Fraser

Vair mi oro van o
Vair mi oro van ee
Vair mi oru o ho
Sad am I without thee.

When I'm lonely my dear heart,
Black the night or wild the sea,
By love's light my foot finds
The old pathway to thee.

Vair mi oro van o
Vair mi oro van ee
Vair mi oru o ho
Sad am I without thee.

Eriskay

I played this tune by memory today! (date) _____

[Eriskay was where Bonnie Prince Charlie first set foot (secretly!)
on Scottish soil in July 1745.]

Tommy's Tip 'Watch out for the surprise rhythm ♪ ♩. and be ready to go back to the fancy repeat sign.' 🐾

Tune 5   **The Dark Island**   *Words: David Silver*
Tune: Iain MacLachlan

Away to the West's where I'm longing to be,
Where the beauty of heaven unfolds by the sea;
Where the deep purple heather blooms
fragrant and free,
On a hilltop high above the Dark Island.

Oh, Isle of my childhood, I'm dreaming of thee,
As the steamer leaves Oban and passes Tiree;
Soon I'll capture the magic that lingers for me,
When I'm back once more upon the Dark Island.

Oh, gentle the sea breeze that ripples the bay,
Where the stream joins the ocean and young
children play;
On the strand of pure silver I'll welcome each day,
And I'll roam for evermore the Dark Island.

Oh, Isle of my childhood, etc.

The Dark Island is Barra in the Outer Hebrides.
Aeroplanes land on its wide sandy beach!

Barra

Tommy's Tip 'Take care with the *triplet* and make this tune loud and strong! Violinists, notice the slurs and use long smooth bow strokes here.'

Tune 6   **Mingulay Boat Song**

Words: Hugh S. Roberton
Tune: Traditional

* higher note for recorder

Permission kindly granted by Roberton Publications

Hill you ho, boys; let her go, boys;
Bring her head round, now all together.
Hill you ho, boys; let her go, boys;
Sailing home, home to Mingulay.

The remote island of Mingulay is now completely deserted.

Tune 7

Ho-ree, Ho-ro
(A Tiree Love Song)

Words: Hugh S. Roberton
Tune: Alexander Sinclair

Happily, quite fast

Permission kindly granted by Roberton Publications

Tommy's Tip 'Once you know this tune try to play it quite fast! You can sway to the music in the chorus – I do! (Violinists, can you find the four C♮s?)' 🐾

Tune 8   **Westering Home**

Words and verse music: Hugh S. Roberton
Chorus: Traditional

* higher note for recorder

Permission kindly granted by Roberton Publications

Westering home, and a song in the air,
Light in the eye, and it's good-bye to care;
Laughter o' love, and a welcoming there;
Isle of my heart, my own one!

Tell me o' lands o' the Orient gay!
Speak o' the riches and joys o' Cathay!
Eh, but it's grand to be wakin' each day
To find yourself nearer to *Isla*. (And it's)

Westering home, and a song etc.

Where are the folk like the folk o' the west?
Canty, and *couthy*, and kindly, the best;
There I would *hie* me, and there I would rest
At *hame* wi' my *ain* folk in Isla. (And it's)

Westering home, and a song etc.

Isla: usually spelt Islay   canty: cheerful
couthy (pronounced koothy): homely, pleasant
hie: hurry   hame: home   ain: own

Islay

Tommy's Tip 'This is a very gentle tune, so play and sing it softly and smoothly (in musical language *piano* means soft and *legato* means smooth!)' 🐾

Tune 9   Iona Boat Song

Words: Hugh S. Roberton
Tune: Traditional

* higher note for recorder

Permission kindly granted by Roberton Publications

Softly glide we along, softly chant we our song,
For a king who to resting is come:
O beloved and best, thou'rt faring out west,
To the dear Isle Iona, thy home.

Hum the tune again and then repeat the verse.

Iona is famous for its Abbey and its associations with Saint Columba who chose to settle here and establish Christianity in Scotland. Legend says that this tune was sung by the monks of long ago as they rowed the dead Scottish kings and chiefs to their resting place on the island – forty-eight kings and chiefs are said to be buried here! Isn't that amazing?

Iona

Tommy's Tip 'Notice the repeat signs. Violinists, make sure your bow moves smoothly as it crosses the strings – no jerks!' 🐾

Tune 10   Joy of my Heart

Words: Hugh S. Roberton
Tune: Traditional

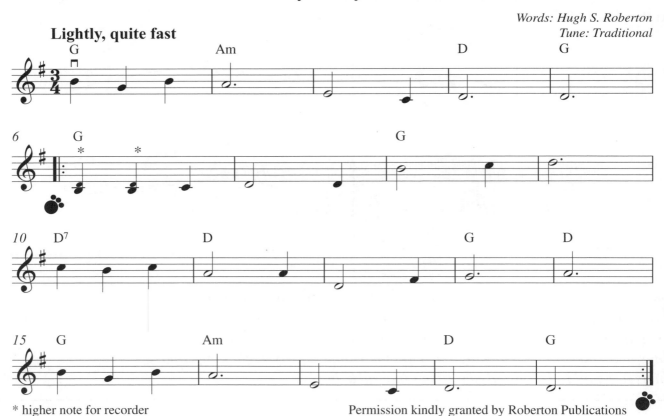

* higher note for recorder

Permission kindly granted by Roberton Publications

Joy of my heart, Isle of *Moola*!
Whither I wander east or west,
Waking or dreaming, thou art near me;
Joy of my heart, Isle of Moola!

Sing ye o' the *Coolins* of Skye,
Of Harris, or *Eigg*, or fair Iona.
Joy of my heart, Isle of Moola!

Whither I wander east or west,
Waking or dreaming, thou art near me;
Joy of my heart, Isle of Moola!

Moola: Mull
Coolins (usually spelt Cuillins): the Cuillin Hills
Eigg is pronounced Egg

Tommy's Quiz

Tommy wonders what you've discovered about the music and the tunes in this book. Check with your teacher if you've got all the answers right. Good luck!

1. Who helped Bonnie Prince Charlie escape to Skye?_____

2. How many tunes use the repeat sign :‖?_____

3. On which island were kings and chiefs buried?_____

4. In musical language what word means soft or quiet?_____

5. How many islands are mentioned in Tune 10? _____

6. Which tune uses lots of 'Scotch snap' rhythms? _____

7. Where do planes land on the beach? _____

8. How many notes make the 'triplet' in the Mingulay Boat Song? _____

9. Can you find Tommy at tune six? What is he doing?_____

10. Which tune is the Memory Tune? Can you play it by memory yet?_____

'Well done! See you soon.'   Love Tommy 🐾

PS 'Try to find the islands on the map beside Tune 1. Some of them are **very** small, so why not look at a bigger map of Scotland and find them there!' 🐾